This book belongs to:

Name _sarah_

Age _6_

My favourite Disney character is:

B Bush Leia year

Editor: Anne Ewart   Designer: Martin Shubrook

£5.99
UK only

D1458504

Disney and Me Annual 2001

Contents

Peter Pan

The Lion King

Aladdin

The Little Mermaid

Dinosaur

Competition

The elephant's hair

Tarzan's best friend, Terk, was going exploring in the jungle with two of her gorilla playmates, Flynt and Mungo. Tarzan wanted to go with them and join in their adventure but

Mungo and Flynt didn't want Tarzan tagging along behind. "He's too small to be any fun. We'll have to keep stopping to let him catch up with us," they said.

Terk knew how to get rid of Tarzan. "If you want to join in with us, you have to bring back an elephant's hair from the lagoon at the bottom of the waterfall!" she said.

Terk and her friends thought that Tarzan would give up and go home, but they were wrong. Tarzan let out a big yell as he rushed past them and leaped into the lagoon.

Tarzan began swimming towards the herd of elephants. "Piranhas! Everybody run!" yelled Tantor, a nervous, young elephant, when he saw Tarzan under the water.

Suddenly, Tarzan jumped up and grabbed one of the elephants' tails. The whole herd trumpeted in panic and began to splash about and stampede out of the lagoon.

Up on the cliff, Terk, Flynt and Mungo watched, as the herd of elephants charged right through the area where the other gorillas were feeding. "Oh, no, look at the trouble we've caused! We shouldn't have set Tarzan such an impossible task!" groaned Terk. They rushed down to the lagoon to make sure that Tarzan was all right.

When they reached him, Tarzan held out his hand. "I did it! I got the elephant's hair. Can I join in with you now?" he spluttered. The three gorillas gasped in amazement.

"Be careful, that piranha will bite you!" cried Tantor, still thinking that Tarzan was dangerous. "Tarzan's not a piranha. He's an ape, just like us," replied Terk, smiling.

About the story

1. What are Terk's friends' names?
2. Why did Terk ask Tarzan to fetch an elephant's hair?
3. How did Tarzan get into the lagoon?
4. Who thought Tarzan was a piranha?
5. Where did the elephant herd charge through?

Answers:
1) Flynt and Mungo. 2) She thought that Tarzan would give up and go home. 3) Tarzan leaped off the cliff. 4) Tantor. 5) The gorillas' feeding area.

Jungle search

Tarzan and his friends have gone exploring in the jungle. Can you count how many butterflies and bananas they saw on their travels?

Answer: Five butterflies and eight bananas.

A splashing time

Tarzan has completed the tough challenge set by Terk and her friends.
Now it's your turn to complete these tricky teasers.

1 Which gorilla is holding up three fingers?

2 Which two flowers add up to the same amount?

3 What type of creature is swimming under the water?

4 How many elephants can you count?

5 Is Tarzan holding the hair in his left or right hand?

6 Can you spot five differences in Tantor's reflection?

Aping around

Jane loves playing with the baby gorillas. Join in with their fun by finding the answers to these three puzzles.

1 Which of these close-ups doesn't appear in the picture?

a

b

c

d

2 Starting with **JANE**, put these words in order so that only one letter changes each time.

JANE CANS CANE PINS PANS

3 Can you think of three names beginning with J to call the baby gorillas

A jungle journal

Jane likes to write about her jungle adventures in her journal. Help her finish writing about her day by using the spare words on the page to fill in the blank spaces.

baboons

fruit

pencils

I was looking at some beautiful when I spotted a eating some .

I drew a picture of it in my with my . Suddenly, lots of other  appeared. My, what a sight!

butterflies

book

baby baboon

Picture

Put the pictures in order to match the toys' story. What other adventures do you think the toys had while they were looking for Woody?

THE STORY

1) **The toys watched through the binoculars as Woody was stolen by a greedy toy collector.**

2) **By decoding some letters from the toy collector's car, Buzz found out that Woody had been taken to Al's Toy Barn.**

3) **The toys had great fun driving around Al's Toy Barn, looking for Woody. But they couldn't find him!**

4) **The toys went to look for Woody in the toy collector's apartment, high up in a block of flats.**

5) **Eventually, the toys found Woody and some new friends, too - Bullseye the horse and Jessie the cowgirl.**

6) **The toys made it back to Andy's room... just in time to welcome Andy back from Cowboy Camp!**

a

c

e

Answers:
1) a. 2) e. 3) f. 4) b. 5) c. 6) d.

perfect

b

d

f

Ready, set, go!

Buzz and his friends are on an exciting adventure to rescue Woody. Play this game with your friends to see who will be the champion cone carrier.

START 1 2 3 4

drop

11 10 go 8 7 6

12

13 14 drop

16

go

18 19 20 21

You will need: a dice and a counter for each player.

How to play

Place all the counters at the start, next to Buzz. Take turns to roll the dice and move your counter along the numbered spaces. If you land on a **drop** space you must miss a turn. If you land on a **go** space you must move forward one space. The first person to reach Woody is the winner, but watch out for the chewing gum!

29 30 **31** drop

SPLAT! Go back to START.

33

27

34

go

go

25

36

FINISH

24

37

41

23

38 drop 40

Toy teasers

There's always something going on when the toys are in town. Can you answer each of these tricky toy teasers?

1 Which shadow matches Jessie exactly?

a   b   c   d

2 Draw a line to match each of these words to what they are.

slurp ·   · a gooey ooze

slug ·   · how a snake moves

slime ·   · a slimy creature

slither ·   · a drinking noise

3 Can you help Slinky think of four more words that begin with "**sl**"?

Answers: 1) a. 2) slurp - a drinking noise, slug - a slimy creature, slime - a gooey ooze, slither - how a snake moves.

18

The one and only

Buzz Lightyear has been surrounded by impostors! Can you spot the real Buzz Lightyear? He is the only one that matches his picture exactly.

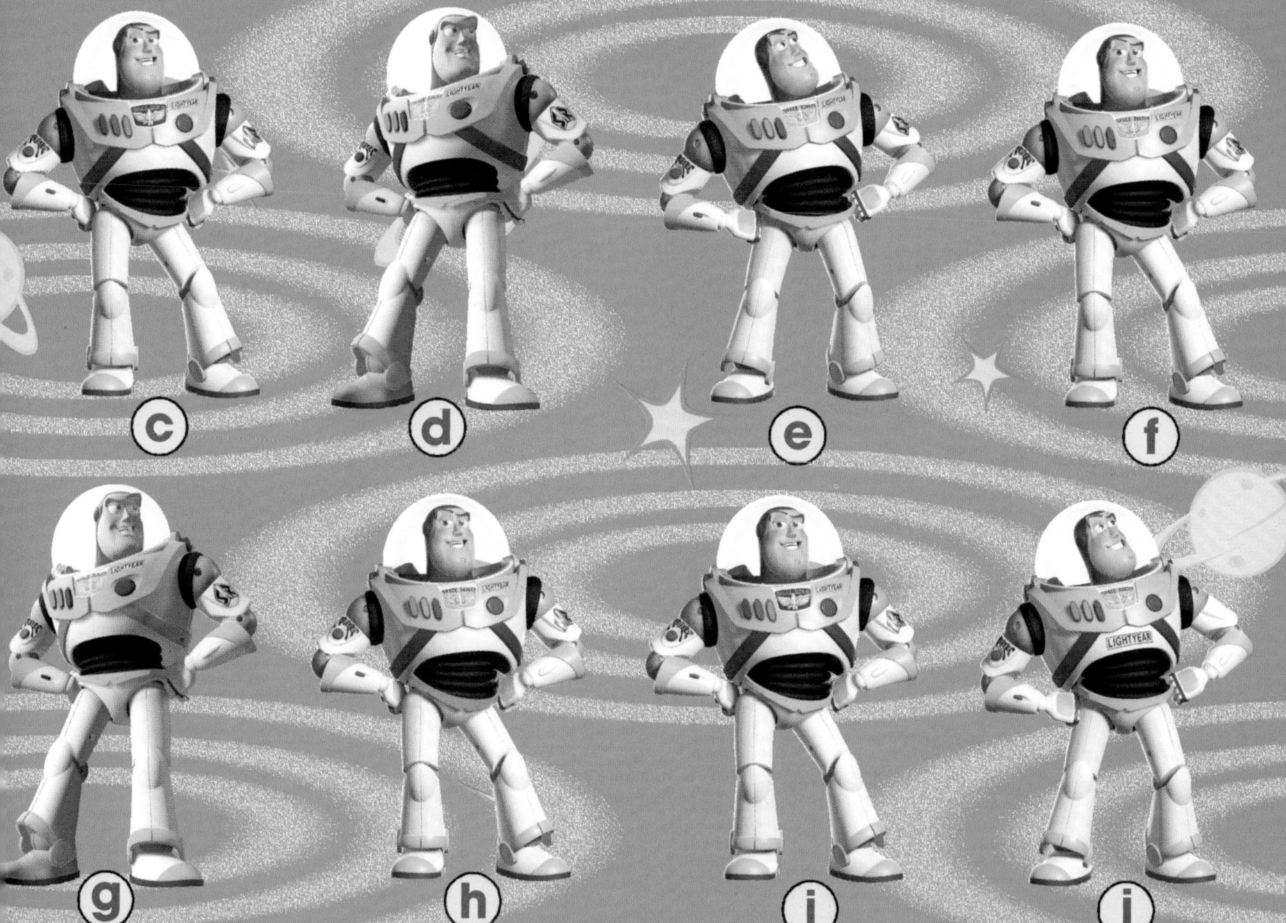

(a)

(b)

(c)

(d)

(e)

(f)

(g)

(h)

(i)

(j)

Answer: j

Dalmatian-itis

The Baduns had captured the puppies in Hell Hall, and had spent all afternoon teasing them. "We might as well have a bit of a snooze before Cruella arrives," said Jasper. Horace and Jasper slumped into big armchairs and fell asleep. "Let's teach those two big bullies a lesson," said Patch, as he explored the room.

Patch had a look in one of the drawers. He wagged his tail and whispered, "Hey, come and see what I've found." The puppies all rushed over to have a look.

When Jasper woke up, he felt a bit hungry. He reached over for his sandwich and took a bite. "Yuk!" he shouted. "This sandwich is covered with spots!"

"Blugh! My sandwiches must have gone off," said Jasper. "I need to have a drink." He went to take a drink, but the bottle was spotty as well! Jasper quickly went over to Horace. "I think we've been around these horrible puppies too long," he said. "Their spots are catching!" The puppies giggled.

"Don't be daft," laughed Horace. "You can't catch Dalmatian spots." "Then why do you have them on your face?" asked Jasper sarcastically.

"You do, too," snapped Horace. "We've got Dalmatian-itis!" shrieked Jasper. "Cruella will make coats out of us if she sees these spots!" cried Horace.

The puppies crowded around Jasper and Horace. "Keep away from us!" they shouted as they unlocked the door and ran out. The puppies rolled about laughing. "Jasper and Horace will kick themselves when they realise that their Dalmatian-itis is only ink that we flicked on them with our tails!"

About the story

1. Where were the Baduns keeping the puppies?
2. What was wrong with Jasper's sandwich?
3. Where were Horace's spots?
4. What did the Baduns think they had caught?
5. What really made the spots?

Spots and dots

The Dalmatian puppies find spots and dots wherever they go!
Here are some dotty puzzles for you to discover.

1. Look at the white squares on the left for ten seconds. Then look at the black squares on the right. Dark spots will magically appear where the white lines cross.

2. Is the square with the thick line on the side of the box, or on the bottom? If you stare at the spot, the box will keep changing every few seconds.

Cruella's visit

Cruella wants to buy the puppies,
but Roger and Anita have told her that the puppies are not for sale!

1 Which puppy is being held by Cruella?

a

b

a   b   c   d   e

2 Which of these objects is not in the scene?

3 What time is it?

4 How many flowers are there?

5 Which of these bags belongs to Cruella?

b

d

c

a

e

c

Answers:
1.b 2.d 3.4:00 4.15 5.d

25

Mulan's army

Mulan and three other soldiers had been sent across the mountains to collect supplies for the army camp. As they made their way back towards the camp with their full cart, they came to a narrow path. "Let's stop here and have something to eat," said Mulan. She cut up a loaf of bread and spread honey on the slices.

As they ate, Mulan heard something. "What's that noise?" she asked the other soldiers. Everyone stopped eating and listened. There was a faint rumbling sound which was becoming louder and louder. Soon the noise was louder than thunder and it was making the ground shake.

Mulan looked up and shouted, "Look out, everyone! It's an avalanche!" They all hid under the cart as huge boulders tumbled past them and disappeared down the side of the mountain. The very last boulder to fall crashed on to the road right in front of their cart. It completely blocked the path. "Oh no!" cried Ling. "How are we going to get the supplies back to the camp?"

Yao replied, "If we use our strength, we'll soon shift it." They all began to push as hard as they could. They groaned and grunted, but the boulder didn't even move an inch. Yao looked at Mulan and said, "If you weren't so skinny, we would be able to move it."

Ling shook his head and said, "It's not anyone's fault. We'd need a whole army to shift that lump." Chien-Po sighed and said, "And to make matters worse, my bread and honey has been covered in dirt!" Yao, Ling and Chien-Po tried to push the boulder again.

Mulan looked at the slices of bread on the ground. She was amazed when one of the tiny ants crawled under a slice of bread and lifted it up. Mulan suddenly knew exactly what to do to move the boulder. She rummaged in the back of the cart and found a large pot. Then she climbed on to the boulder and said, "Stand back, everyone!" Mulan tipped the pot, and a gallon of honey poured over the boulder.

The honey slowly dribbled down the sides of the boulder. "How is making it sticky going to make the boulder any easier to move?" asked Ling. Mulan smiled and said, "You said we'd need a whole army to move it, and you were right!"

As she spoke, the little ant reappeared. But this time it was followed by hundreds of other ants. They marched straight towards the honey-coated boulder and surrounded it. Within moments, the group of ants had lifted up the boulder and carried it away. Mulan and the others jumped into the cart and carried on towards the army camp. Yao nudged Mulan and grinned, "You may not have very strong muscles, but you have a very strong mind!"

the end

Rice riddles

Mulan is working hard, but she can still find time for some fun and games!

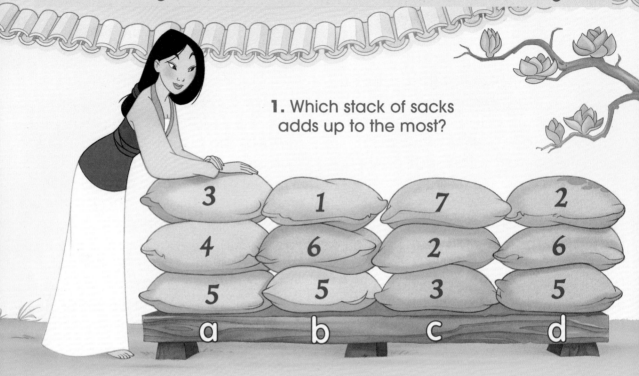

1. Which stack of sacks adds up to the most?

a	b	c	d
3	1	7	2
4	6	2	6
5	5	3	5

2. Little Brother weighs 6 kilograms. Which two sacks will balance the scale?

2kg
3kg
4kg
5kg

3. Is there an odd or even amount of rice grains?

28

Mushu's mysteries

When he's not causing mischief, Mushu likes to solve perplexing puzzles.
See if you can help him find the answers to these three teasers.

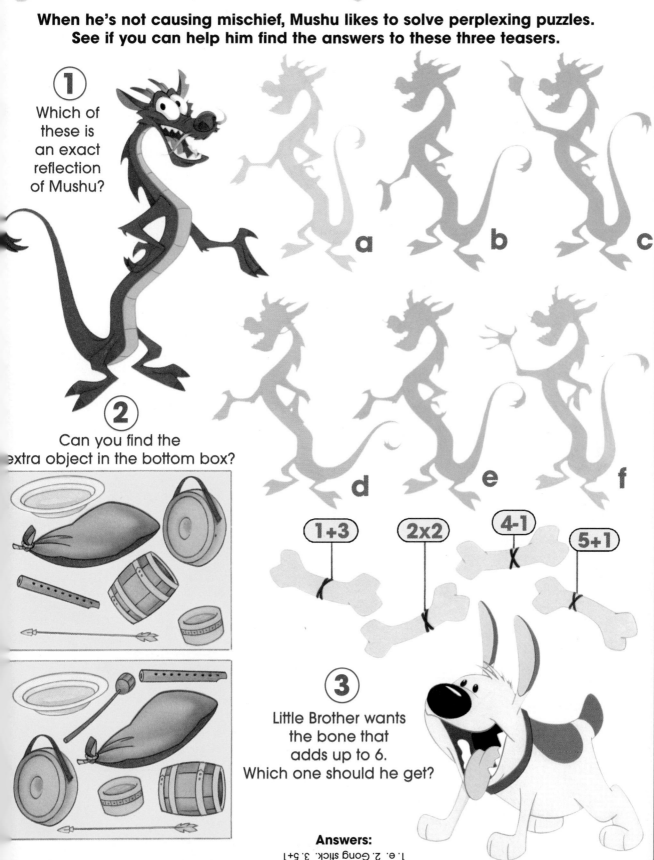

① Which of these is an exact reflection of Mushu?

a   b   c

d   e   f

② Can you find the extra object in the bottom box?

1+3   2x2   4-1   5+1

③ Little Brother wants the bone that adds up to 6. Which one should he get?

Spot the spy

Captain Shang has found out there is a Hun spy amongst his men, but he isn't sure which one it is. Can you help Shang find the spy by using the clues below?

The Hun spy is standing to the left of the soldier who is six places to the right of Mulan.

Answer: soldier g.

30

Mulan's map

Like all good soldiers, Mulan can read a map.
Why don't you try? If you were standing where the X is on the
map, which directions would the four views
at the bottom be - north, south, east or west?

Answers
1. South. 2. West. 3. North. 4. East.

Fight fair and square

It looks like Captain Hook has failed to outsmart Peter Pan yet again!
Are you smart enough to find the three pairs of identical squares?

Answer: 1a and 1g, 8a and 9c, 8b and 9g.

Hook can't lift a book

Peter Pan has challenged Captain Hook to pick up a book. Hook thought it would be easy, but it's much harder than it looks!

You will need two metres of strong string and a heavy book.

1. Tie the string around the book.

2. Ask each of your friends to stand up, one at a time, and hold one end of the string in each hand.

3. Now challenge them to pull the string out straight, while lifting the book at the same time.

4. No matter how hard they try, they will not be able to keep the string straight and lift the book.

When Captain Hook and his crew are not chasing Peter Pan, they are out hunting for treasure to fill their pirate's chest. Why not make your very own treasure chest to store all your valuables? Be sure to ask a grown-up to help you.

What you will need:
2 cardboard boxes
scissors
a pen or pencil
glue
masking tape
paints
string

1 Cut off one large flap, and both small ones.

Cut open the second box, leaving the bottom, and two short sides. Draw a half-circle on each of the short sides. Don't throw away the long side you have cut off.

2

3

Cut around the curves of the two half-circles. Fold them back into an upright position. Take one of the long sides you cut away and tape it down the centre for support.

asure chest

4 Cut a 24inch, or 60cm square of cardboard. Carefully bend it over the frame you have made. Glue the sides down and secure with masking tape.

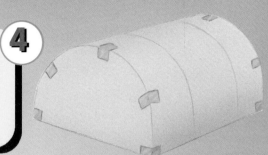

5 On the first box, cut a square away from the middle of the remaining flap, to make two hinges. Glue the lid on to the hinges and leave to dry.

6 Paint the outside of the chest with a keyhole and some pirate designs. Add different coloured sticky tape, to create a barrel effect.

7 Finally, line the chest with red cloth or shiny paper. Fix some string to each side of the lid. Now you are ready to fill your personal pirate treasure chest!

Rough and tumble

Peter Pan and The Lost Boys play all day long!
Join in with them as they find fun in the forest.

Cubby

Rabbit

1 Whose arrow will hit the bull's-eye?

② How many arrows can you find?

③ Where is Peter's shadow?

④ Which sword is the longest?

⑤ Who is winning the tug of war?

⑥ Whose names are on the signpost?

OHOK

HOJN

ENTBILLREK

LICMAEH

YDNWE

b

Answers:
1. Cubby's. 2. Twelve. 3. On the tree. 4. They are both the same. 5. a. 6. HOOK, JOHN, TINKERBELL, MICHAEL, WENDY.

The flying lion

Simba was out exploring one day, and as usual, Zazu was following him. "I'll be able to go wherever I want when I'm king," said Simba. "Not necessarily," boasted Zazu.

Zazu landed on a rock and added, "For instance, a lion can't fly to the top of a tree, like I can." Then he flew up to the highest branch in a nearby tree.

"I'll teach Zazu not to be such a show-off," Simba thought to himself. He began to walk away towards the watering hole to find one of his friends.

"I'm still watching you, Simba!" Zazu called down from the tree. "Well, I'm not going very far," said Simba. Zazu watched as Simba walked along the watering hole.

But the hot afternoon sun began to make Zazu feel very drowsy. "I'll just take a short nap," thought Zazu, as he snuggled in the leaves.

"Hello, Zazu!" said Simba. "I thought I'd fly up here and join you for a nap!" Zazu nearly fell out of the tree with shock. "I must be dreaming," he thought.

Zazu rubbed his eyes in disbelief, "A flying lion? The heat of the sun has played tricks with my mind." Zazu flew off in a fluster to look for some shade.

But Simba didn't really fly up to the top of the tree - a tall giraffe lifted Simba up! "That will keep Zazu from boasting that he's the only one who can fly," laughed Simba.

Jungle jigsaw

There's been a bit of a mix-up with these three Pride Land pictures.
Can you find where the nine jigsaw pieces belong?

40

Zebra crossing

Help Simba reach Nala
by finding the way
through the white stripes on the zebras.

The feast finders

Timon and Pumba have found a feast of bugs!
See if you can solve all of these tasty puzzles.

1 What number should go in the blank space?

1
10
31
11
30
21 20

2 Which caterpillar adds up to the highest number?

a 3 2 3 7
b 1 2 5
c 3 4 2
d 7 1 3

a b c d e f

3 Which of these details does not appear in the picture?

4 Which two butterflies are the same?

5 How many berries are in the bushes?

6 How many bugs with red spots can you count?

Answers:
1. 40. 2. a. 3. e. 4. d and g. 5. 11. 6. Two.

43

A charming tail

One afternoon, Aladdin and Abu were walking through Agrabah's market. They noticed a large crowd of people watching a snake charmer. "Come on, Abu, this looks like good fun!" said Aladdin.

The snake charmer sat cross-legged on the ground holding a small flute in his hands. In front of him was a wicker basket. The snake charmer began playing the flute. As the music filled the air, the head of a deadly-looking snake rose out of the basket. The snake stretched up and began to sway and dance along to the tune. The trembling crowd gasped in amazement. But Abu wasn't watching the snake charmer or the snake - he was looking at a group of guards who were in the crowd. One of them was eating a big, juicy apple. It looked so delicious that Abu climbed up a wall and dangled down right above the guard's head. "Oh, no," thought Aladdin, "Abu's going to get us into trouble!" When the guard went to take another bite of the apple, Abu swung in front of him and bit it first. The guard drew his sword and shouted, "Catch that monkey!" Abu jumped into Aladdin's arms and the guards rushed forward. "I think it's time we left," gulped Aladdin. He sprinted off through the market.

Aladdin realised that the guards were still following close behind. "We won't be able to out-run them, Abu," said Aladdin. "I'd better think of something fast!" Aladdin spotted a stall that had some old junk on it - this gave Aladdin an idea. He grabbed an old pot and a straw and ran around the corner. He put the pot on the ground and said, "Quick, Abu, climb inside!" Abu dived into the pot and curled up at the bottom. Just then, the angry guards came charging around the corner and saw Aladdin by the pot. "The monkey must be hiding in there!" said one of the guards. They raised their swords and got ready to move in. Aladdin sat cross-legged on the ground and said, "Don't get too close to the dangerous snake in the pot - its bite is deadlier than a hundred sharp swords!" The guards looked nervously at each other. "Don't listen to him," the leader shouted, "there's no snake in there! He's just protecting the monkey."

When the guards stepped forward, Aladdin put the straw to his mouth and began to whistle down it. The guard shrieked when a long snake-like shape rose up from the pot and began swaying to the tune. "There *is* a snake in there!" one of the guards said. All the guards backed away and decided to look elsewhere for Abu. When they were gone, Aladdin laughed and said, "It's safe to come out, Abu. Lucky for you they didn't get close enough to notice that the deadly snake was really just your wiggling tail!"

the end

45

Reach the lamp

Who will win the race to get to the magical lamp?
If Jafar gets there before Aladdin or Abu,
it will mean big trouble for everyone in Agrabah!
Play this game on your own or with two friends.

How to play

Place a counter on each of the three characters. Take turns flipping a coin. If it shows heads, you move up a number. If it shows tails you move down a number. The first character to reach the lamp is the winner!

5

4

3

3

2

1

1

Aladdin

Jafar

Abu

Ribbon route

Aladdin has a secret meeting with Jasmine, but he could end up in big trouble if he follows some of these ribbons. Which ribbon should Aladdin follow to reach Jasmine safely?

a   b   c   d   e   f

Answer: Ribbon e.

A date with the Genie

The Genie knows a magical mathematical trick that will impress all your friends.

Take a calendar and ask a friend to choose any three dates in a row.
For example, 3, 4, 5, or 26, 27, 28. They must not tell you the dates they have chosen.

Ask them to add the three dates together and give you the total. After a moment you can tell them the dates they chose.

How it's done

When they tell you the total, divide it by 3. This will give you the middle date. Take one away to get the date before it, and add one to get the date after it!

The boogle bopper

Ariel and Flounder were exploring an old shipwreck when they found a kite. Ariel had never seen a kite before. "I wonder what this pretty thing does," she said. "Why don't we ask Scuttle? He always knows about human stuff," said Flounder. The pair of them took the kite and swam up to the surface to find Scuttle.

Scuttle looked at the kite for a long time, trying to figure out what it was. Finally, he cleared his throat and announced, "This object is a boogle bopper!"

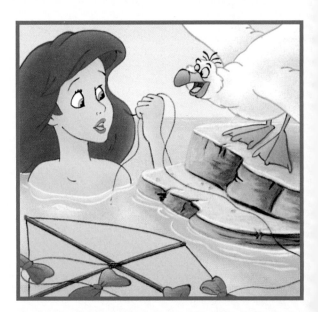

"A boogle bopper? What's that?" asked Ariel. Scuttle scratched his head. "Erm, sailors use it to find out how deep the sea is. Go ahead, try it out," he said.

Ariel and Flounder took the string of the kite and swam deeper and deeper under the sea until they reached the bottom. Then Ursula appeared.

"What are you holding?" hissed Ursula. "It's a boogle bopper!" blurted Flounder. "Anything found in this part of the sea belongs to me!" said Ursula.

"In fact," she went on, "I've just found you in my part of the sea, so now you belong to me as well!" She lurched forward and tried to grab Ariel.

"It's no use trying to escape," laughed Ursula. "I'll catch you!" Ariel and Flounder swam up to the surface as fast as they could, but Ursula was close behind.

Just as Ursula was catching up to Ariel, a big gust of wind lifted the kite out of the water. The string from the kite pulled Ursula backwards, way out to sea!

As Ursula disappeared into the distance, Scuttle appeared. "Erm, I forgot to mention that the boogle bopper also gets rid of nasty sea witches!"

About the story

1. What did Ariel and Flounder find?
2. What did Scuttle say it was used for?
3. Why didn't Ursula catch Ariel?
4. What colour is the kite?

Answers:
1) A kite. 2) To find out how deep the sea is. 3) Because the kite pulled her out to sea. 4) Orange.

Sebastian's checklist

In the top picture, Sebastian is making a note of all the visitors who are entering the royal palace. The bottom picture shows them leaving. Which creatures aren't on Sebastian's checklist?

Answer:
9 and 13.

Clam-a-lama

Ariel and her friends are trying to put the clam shells back together. See if you can match the halves they are holding to the ones on the seabed.

Underwater wonders

Flounder has found these three
fishy puzzles for you to dive into!
See if you can fish out the answers.

a
b
c
d
e
f
g
h

1 Which seaweed is the longest?

8
1
2
7
3
6
4
5

2 How many fish
are in this shoal?

3 Which shadow
matches the fish?

Answers:
1. g. 2. sixteen. 3. 7.

55

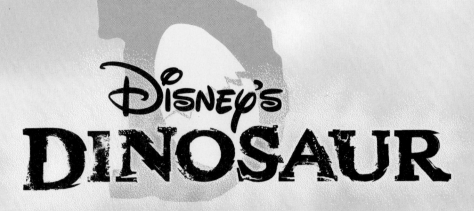

DISNEY'S DINOSAUR

Meet Aladar and his friends from Disney's *Dinosaur* and read all about their exciting adventures!

Aladar is a brave and kind dinosaur. He grew up with Yar and his family of lemurs on a small island, far away from any other dinosaurs. When Aladar left the island and met a herd of dinosaurs, he was amazed to find other creatures that looked just like him!

Aladar

Yar

Yar is a wise, old Lemur who has a daughter called **Plio**, and a granddaughter called **Suri**. Aladar is part of their lemur family, even though he doesn't look anything like them! There is also cheeky **Zini**, who is always causing trouble!

Plio

Eema

Baylene

Url

Url is Eema's and Baylene's pet dinosaur. He can be a little shy if he doesn't know you very well.

Eema and **Baylene** are two old dinosaurs at the back of the Herd. When Aladar and the lemurs join the Herd, Eema and Baylene are both very kind to them.

Neera is the sister of Kron, the Herd's leader. Aladar and Neera become very good friends, even though Neera's brother doesn't like it very much.

Neera

Zini

The story

A long, long time ago, a small furry lemur, named Plio, found a large egg sitting on the branch of a tree. Plio watched as the egg cracked open and a strange-looking creature peered out.

Plio's father, Yar, came to have a look. "Well, what is it?" asked Yar.

"It *was* an egg," replied Plio, as she held the baby in her arms.

The lemurs named the baby Aladar and before long the baby had grown into a huge dinosaur! Aladar was very big, but he was also very gentle. He had great fun playing with all his tiny lemur friends.

Lemur Island was a happy place, until one day a huge comet fell to earth, destroying the island!

Aladar and the lemurs were forced to swim across the sea to a new land. There, they met a huge herd of dinosaurs, led by an iguanodon called Kron. Aladar was amazed to see so many creatures that looked just like him!

Aladar and the lemurs were quite scared of the dinosaurs, but then they met two old dinosaurs, called Baylene and Eema, who were very kind to them. They told Aladar that the Herd was on its yearly journey to the Nesting Grounds.

Baylene and Eema were finding it hard to keep up with the rest of the Herd, so Aladar asked Kron to slow the Herd down. But Kron wouldn't listen. Neera, Kron's sister, was very impressed by Aladar's kindness to the other

dinosaurs and soon Neera and Aladar became friends.

As the Herd continued on their journey, Kron realised that some fierce dinosaurs, called carnotaurs, were following close behind. Kron ordered the Herd to move even faster.

Baylene and Eema couldn't keep up, so Aladar stayed behind to look after them. Neera had to go on with the rest of the Herd.

Aladar led Baylene, Eema and the lemurs into a big, dark cave where they could hide from the carnotaurs.

As they walked towards the back of the cave, Zini smelled fresh air! They all started pulling rocks away from the back of the cave until finally, they broke through the cave wall. There in front of them was the beautiful green valley of the Nesting Grounds!

Aladar and his friends walked into the Nesting Grounds, but then Eema and Baylene realised that the usual entrance to the Nesting Grounds was blocked! Unless the rest of the Herd went through the cave, they would never be able to reach the valley. Aladar decided that he must go back and tell Neera and the others.

When Aladar found the Herd, Kron was trying to make them climb up a very dangerous cliff. "I know a way to the valley, and everybody can make it!" cried Aladar, but Kron wouldn't listen.

While Kron argued with Aladar, an evil carnotaur came roaring towards them. Aladar told the Herd to stand together and fight as one, but Kron wouldn't listen. The whole Herd roared together and the carnotaur became quite scared. But then, the carnotaur noticed Kron standing all on his own and chased after him. Aladar and Neera tried to save Kron, but they were too late.

Aladar and Neera called the Herd together and led them through the cave and into the Nesting Grounds. By working together and with Aladar's courage, the Herd had found a beautiful and safe new home!

the end

You could win a fantastic family break to

Win!  Win!

DISNEYLAND® PARIS

Visitors young and old can discover the magic of Disneyland® Paris with its Theme Park, its seven themed hotels and of course Disney® Village, the entertainment centre.

The Prize: includes two nights bed and breakfast for a family of four at one of the fabulous Disneyland Paris themed hotels*, plus three days unlimited entry into the Disneyland Park.

2001 will be the best year ever at Disneyland Paris!

In addition to over 50 amazing attractions, rides and shows, this year at Disneyland Paris there will be the most fantastic seasonal festivals for you and your family to enjoy!

The year starts off magically at Disneyland Paris, as from January until March 2001 Kids Go Free to the magic. In March you can enjoy all the craic of the Celtic Festival or salsa the night away in the Festival Latino. Summer is always magical at Disneyland Paris and then before you know it... Trick or Treat! Welcome to HalloweenLand! Then, the following month brings the fantastic Bonfire Spectacular Celebrations. Also from November, until the end of the year, it's the magic of a Very Merry Disney® Christmas all wrapped up at Disneyland Paris just for you!

Come and experience the magic in 2001 at Disneyland Paris
Disneyland Paris, The Magic is Closer Than You Think.
**For more information on Disneyland Paris call: 08705 030303
or visit: www.disney.co.uk**

How to Enter:

Unscramble these letters to spell out the name of Mickey's pet dog : LTPOU

Send your answer, along with your name and address to:

Egmont World Ltd,
Deanway Technology Centre,
Wilmslow Road,
Handforth,
Cheshire SK9 3FB.

The closing date for entries is the 12th January 2001.

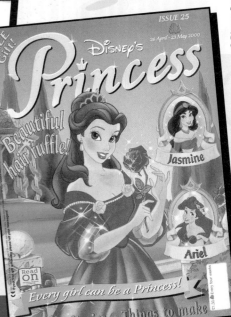